Charlie's Blue Boots

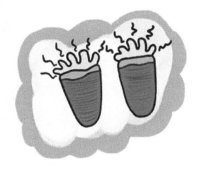

Written by
Charlie Higdon and Judye James

Illustrated by
Aerin Rhoades

This is Charlie. He is almost five years old. He has a big smile and curly blonde hair.

He has a twin sister named Frances and a big brother named Eric.

His mom and dad love him very much.

Charlie is also a Little Person. That means he is shorter than a lot of people, but he doesn't care. He's very happy with who he is. Still, growing up can be hard.

Charlie's legs are bowed.
This makes him walk
like a cowboy entering
a saloon. His mom and
dad wondered if he could
have straight legs and
could someday walk like
everyone else.

They found a doctor named
Michael who is very good at
straightening people's legs.

Charlie and his family got on a big plane and flew to Baltimore where the doctor lives.

During their office appointment, Doctor Michael told Charlie and his parents that he could straighten Charlie's legs and help him walk better.

Charlie's parents decided this was the best for Charlie, and they made an appointment for his surgery right away.

When the time came for the surgery, Mom and Dad loaded up the car and took Charlie back to Baltimore. It was a long drive.

Frances stayed with her grandmother. She knew
she would miss her twin brother. She went to school,
gymnastics, and church while Charlie was gone, but life
wasn't as much fun without him. Big brother Eric was
in high school, so he cheered Charlie on from home.

The day before the surgery, Mom and Dad took
Charlie to a big zoo. He loved seeing all the animals.

He even bought a stuffed panda for Frances.
He missed his sister, but they talked to each
other every day on the telephone.

The next day, Charlie went to
the hospital very early in the
morning. He met Nurse Kelly,
Nurse Molly, and Nurse Robin,
who would take care of him
after the surgery.

They gave him a gown, a hat, and a pair of shoes all made of paper. Charlie loved showing everyone his "new outfit."

Then he received special medicine to help him sleep. His mother carried him to the operating room, where the doctor waited for him. Even though Mom and Dad knew this surgery was the best thing for Charlie, it did not make the long day any easier.

When the surgery was finally over, the nurses took Charlie to a place where they would take care of him while he healed. Charlie was in good hands, so he decided to sleep the rest of the day.

Charlie wore casts that covered his legs. In fact, his toes could barely peak out. Mom chose the casts to be blue, but Charlie didn't like them when he saw them. "I want these blue boots off," he said. It would be a long time before that would happen.

The next morning, Doctor Michael came into Charlie's room to check on him. He asked Charlie to wiggle his toes.

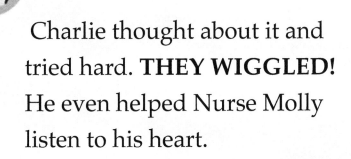

Charlie thought about it and tried hard. **THEY WIGGLED!** He even helped Nurse Molly listen to his heart.

Charlie loved his room in the hospital. He had meals served to him every day, a television for him to watch cartoons, and a big yellow stuffed dog named Josh to keep him company.

After a few days in the hospital, the family drove to Uncle Joe and Aunt Ellen's house. They lived near the hospital. They were glad to see Charlie and had surprises for him. Many friends sent Charlie presents. There were toys, books, videos, games, cookies, candy, and a lot of fun things to do.

Charlie's parents knew they were blessed to have so many friends and family who cared about them. Sometimes, they would take Charlie on a walk around the block in his wheelchair.

When Charlie went back to see Doctor Michael, Charlie was so happy to hear he was healing and could go home the next day. Everyone was glad to go back home, even though Dad had to drive in the rain all the way to Tennessee.

While Charlie was getting well, his
friends came to visit. He could go anywhere
in a stroller or if someone carried him.

The only problem was that he couldn't
stand on his "blue boots." He learned to scoot
around on the floor to get the toys he wanted.

After eight weeks, it was time to go back
to the hospital to get the blue boots off.
A plane took Mom, Dad, and Charlie back
to the hospital to see Doctor Michael.

He was glad to see Charlie and said it was time. Two men came into the room with special saws to remove the casts. Mom sat Charlie in her lap and covered his ears. It did not hurt and was over in just a minute.

The doctor told Charlie and his parents the operation was a success. Although it would be some time before he could walk again, his legs would eventually carry him anywhere he wanted to go.

He could do anything that his legs would let him do. Charlie was ready to get back to being an active five-year-old boy.

He looked forward to hitting the tee-ball, swimming, and playing outside.

He was ready to get moving. He even got a new scooter for his birthday!

Charlie now stands **TALL**. He's proud that his legs work so well, and he can walk much better than before. He's happy his family and friends love him so much.

Charlie is proud to be a **Little Person** who can do anything he sets his mind to do. His body may be short in stature, but his heart and mind are tall enough to allow him to work hard to reach his highest dreams.

Judye James

is Charlie's grandmother and a former teacher. She loves working with Charlie and was the first person to document his unique experiences as a Little Person.

Charlie Higdon

has a type of dwarfism called achondroplasia, but that hasn't stopped him from achieving the same goals as average people, including becoming an Eagle Scout, graduating from The University of Tennessee, and teaching others through his books and blog. Charlie has a big voice in storytelling and cannot wait to share more stories with you.

Instagram: @littlepeople_adventures
Blog: @fantasyfictionandfilm.wordpress.com

Aerin Rhoades

loves to draw and share creative ideas with Charlie and her friends. She studies dramatic writing at Savannah College of Art and Design. When Aerin isn't illustrating or studying, she enjoys escaping reality by watching animated movies.

Instagram: @aerin_josephine
Twitter: @AerinRhoades

To book Aerin and Charlie an event, contact Jody Dyer at **dyer.cbpublishing@gmail.com**

Judye and Charlie at his Eagle Court of Honor

Aerin and Charlie at their high school prom

Crippled Beagle Publishing
Knoxville, Tennessee
dyer.cbpublishing@gmail.com
(865) 414-4017

Printed in the United States of America
Book design by Marcy Gooberman

Bulk orders are available at discounted rates.
Contact the publisher to order.

978-1-970037-42-5

**TO LEARN ABOUT NEW RELEASES, EVENTS,
AND MORE, CONTACT THE PUBLISHER AND FOLLOW:**

@littlepeople_adventures on Instagram

Crippled Beagle Publishing on Facebook

CPSIA information can be obtained
at www.ICGtesting.com
Printed in the USA
BVHW020825060821
613819BV00002B/23